Marco M...

He's a joker wh...
messing abou...
always means ...
if he sometimes gets
things wrong.

Waxy Max

He's very sporty and
football mad. On the
outside, he's tough,
but underneath he's
got the biggest heart.

Philippa Feltpen

A real peacemaker, she
helps keep the other
Pens in order by sorting
out arguments and giving
good advice.

I think we meet
someone new
inside, Splodge.
How exciting!

Squiggle and Splodge

The Scribble twins! They're
both quiet, both shy. Although
they may not look alike, they
do almost everything together.

Enter ...

Helping you to get
to know God more

God Cares

Written by
**Alexa
Tewkesbury**

Every day a short Bible reading is brought to life with the help of the Pens characters. A related question and prayer apply this to daily life. Written in four sections, two focusing on the lives of Pens and two on Bible characters, young children will be inspired to learn more of God and His Word.

What's inside?

CWR

EVERYTHING I NEED

'The LORD is my shepherd; I have everything I need.'
(Psalm 23 v 1)

Sharpy was outside, sniffing.

He sniffed under the fence. He sniffed by the gate. He sniffed behind the dustbin.

That's when he heard it. A whimper.

He peeped round the corner and there it was – something small and puppy-like.

He fetched Max.

'Hello,' smiled Max. 'Who are you?'

There was a name tag on a collar round the puppy-like something's neck: 'Stubbs', it read.

'I think you're lost, Stubbs,' said Max. 'But don't worry. We'll look after you till we find out where you've come from. You're not on your own.'

 Just as Pens take care of Stubbs, so God, the Good Shepherd, takes care of us in every way.

How do you think it might feel to be lost somewhere?

Pens Prayer

Thank You so much, dear Lord, that You look after me and give me everything I need. Amen.

5

Day 2

Everything I Need

'He lets me rest in fields of green grass and leads me to quiet pools of fresh water.' (Psalm 23 v 2)

Found

Stubbs

6

Pens were putting up posters around the town. They announced:

**WE'VE FOUND STUBBS.
IF HE BELONGS TO YOU,
PLEASE SEE MAX.**

'Someone's bound to find you now, Stubbs,' grinned Marco.

'Let's take him to the park with Sharpy,' suggested Charlotte.

Stubbs and Sharpy played and chased each other all over the grass. Now and then they lay down for a rest. Then they jumped into the pond to cool down.

'I think Sharpy really likes Stubbs,' smiled Gloria.

'We *all* like him,' answered Max. 'And he looks much happier now he's had some fun.'

 God, the Good Shepherd, gives us places to play and time to rest, because He knows that's what we need.

Where are your favourite places to play?

Pens Prayer

Heavenly Father, thank You for my playtime and my rest time. Help me remember to spend time with You every day, too. Amen.

7

Day 3

Everything I Need

'He gives me new strength.' (Psalm 23 v 3)

Stubbs' tumble

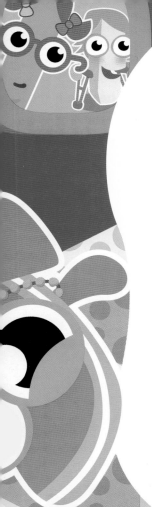

There were paws scampering in and out of Philippa's house.

There were paws pattering round and round Philippa's kitchen.

There were paws dashing up and down Philippa's stairs.

Stubbs was romping about excitedly.

'Slow down!' Philippa called. Suddenly –

THUMP-BUMP-THONK!

Down the stairs Stubbs tumbled, landing with a THUD.

Philippa scooped him up and gave him a huge cuddle.

'You must be more careful,' she said. 'We love you and we want to keep you safe.'

Stubbs felt so much better for being cuddled that he decided to stay exactly where he was – safe in Philippa's arms.

 We can trust in God, the Good Shepherd, completely. He will always be there to comfort us.

Who gives you a cuddle when you hurt yourself?

Pens Prayer

Lord God, thank You for Your loving kindness which gives me new strength. Amen.

It was a sunny afternoon … A warm afternoon … A BEACH afternoon!

'We've got the buckets and spades,' cried Denzil and Charlotte.

'We've got the picnic,' grinned Philippa and Marco.

'We've got the ice-cold drinks,' squealed Squiggle and Splodge.

'We've got Stubbs and Sharpy,' smiled Max and Gloria.

'Now, we don't want you getting lost again, Stubbs,' continued Max, 'so we're going to play "Follow My Leader". Wherever we go, it's important you stay with us. Then you'll get safely to the beach, and safely home again.'

With Pens showing him the way, Stubbs didn't get lost once.

When we follow God, the Good Shepherd, He helps us live every day in the way that's best for us.

When you're out with a grown-up, what can you do to make sure you stay close to them?

Pens Prayer

Dear Father God, I want to do right things, not wrong things. Please teach me to play 'Follow My Leader' with You every day. Amen.

Day 5 Everything I Need

'Even if I go through the deepest darkness, I will not be afraid, LORD …' (Psalm 23 v 4)

It was a dark night … A quiet night … A SCARY night.

At least, it was scary for Stubbs. He'd never been away from home overnight before, or slept anywhere but in his own special basket.

Supposing I have to sleep *downstairs* while Max and Sharpy sleep *upstairs*. Or, worse – supposing I have to sleep OUTSIDE?

Suddenly, Max tickled his ears.

'Time for bed, Stubbs,' he said. 'Up we go. You can share Sharpy's basket.'

Sharpy's basket was just big enough for the two of them. So the scary night wasn't scary after all.

 God, the Good Shepherd, is always beside us.

Is your bedroom upstairs or downstairs? Do you share it with a brother or sister, or is it just for you?

Pens Prayer

Lord God, thank You for watching over me always – even when it's dark. Amen.

Everything I Need

'… for you are with me. Your shepherd's rod and staff protect me.' (Psalm 23 v 4)

Post!

TAP-TAP! There was a knock on Max's front door.

'Good morning!' It was Squiggle and Splodge.

'We were wondering, Max,' they chirped, 'if you'd like us to take Stubbs and Sharpy for a walk.'

'Let's all go,' replied Max. 'I'll just finish breakfast.'

Stubbs sat down by the front door. Suddenly –

FFLOPP! The postman arrived and pushed a handful of letters through Max's letterbox.

PLOMP! They landed on Stubbs' head!

Stubbs shot behind the sofa and huddled there, quivering.

'It's just the post, Stubbs,' soothed Splodge.

'Come on out,' smiled Squiggle. 'You're safe here. We'll make sure of it.'

 A good shepherd keeps his sheep safe. God, our Good Shepherd, keeps us safe, too.

When a letter or card is posted, what needs to be stuck on the envelope?

Pens Prayer

Loving Shepherd, hold my hand every day, I pray. Amen.

Day 7

Everything I Need

'You prepare a banquet for me ... you welcome me as an honoured guest ...' (Psalm 23 v 5)

A Pens' town welcome

Welcom Stubbs

16

Stubbs couldn't help feeling sad.

'Supposing my owner never finds me?' he thought.

'You poor thing,' sighed Charlotte. 'I wish we knew where you lived.'

Denzil's eyes lit up. 'Why don't we give Stubbs a proper Pens' town welcome?' he suggested. 'That's bound to cheer him up.'

So Charlotte hung balloons and Denzil bought delicious treats to eat. Then they invited all their friends to join in the welcome party.

This time it was Stubbs' eyes that lit up.

'You see?' smiled Denzil. 'You're welcome to stay with us for as long as you need to.'

Even when we're feeling sad, God, our Good Shepherd, still fills our lives with good things.

Denzil and Charlotte hold a welcome party for Stubbs. How else could you make a visitor or new friend feel welcome?

Pens Prayer

Father God, thank You that You always welcome me when I want to talk to You. Amen.

'I know that your goodness and love will be with me all my life …' (Psalm 23 v 6)

The thank you something

Stubbs

Stubbs was looking for something.

He scratched under trees and behind bushes. He snuffled through grass. The trouble was, he didn't really know what he was scratching and snuffling for.

Then, he spotted it. A bright, white stone.

'Found something!' he panted excitedly to himself. 'Just the sort of bright, white something that says THANK YOU.'

When he gave the stone to Pens, big, beaming grins spread across their faces. They knew just what Stubbs was trying to say.

'You're very welcome,' smiled Max. 'And thank YOU, Stubbs. We'll always be your special friends.'

 God, our Good Shepherd's love is with us every single day.

If you wanted to give someone a thank you present, what could you give?

Pens Prayer

Dear Lord, I praise You that Your love for me will never end. Amen.

Everything I Need

'… and your house will be my home as long as I live.'
(Psalm 23 v 6)

'Who's that?' wondered Gloria.

Someone she didn't know was walking past the shops.

'Who's that?' wondered Marco.

Someone he didn't know was crossing the park.

'Who's that?' wondered Philippa.

Someone she didn't know was knocking at Max's door.

'I'm Gordon Glue-stick,' announced the visitor, 'I've come to take my Stubbs home.'

Stubbs was so excited, he couldn't keep still. He chased round and round. He jumped up and down.

'I've been so worried,' beamed Gordon. 'Thank you for looking after him.'

'We've LOVED it,' replied Max. 'And Stubbs can come to stay again – whenever he likes.'

 God, our Good Shepherd, invites us to stay with Him always.

How do you think Gordon felt when he found Stubbs?

Pens Prayer

Loving Lord, thank You so much for being my Good Shepherd. I want to live every day with You. Amen.

A PLACE TO BE SAFE
The baby in the basket

Day 10

'… a new king … came to power in Egypt.'
(Exodus 1 v 8)

A dreadful thing

22

God's friends, the Israelites, were living in a country called Egypt. But Egypt's new king was worried.

'I don't like these Israelites,' he said to his people. 'There are too many of them. They might try to take over our country.'

So the king did something terrible. He ordered that all the Israelite baby boys should be killed.

'What a dreadful thing!' cried the Israelite families.

But one Israelite mother decided there and then, 'No one's going to take away *my* baby boy. Not even a king.'

God's friends were in trouble, but God had a plan to help them.

Who do you know who isn't friends with God yet? You could pray for them this week.

Pens Prayer

Thank You, my Father, that You always want to help us when we're in trouble. Amen.

A Place to be Safe
The baby in the basket

Day 11

'When she saw what a fine baby he was, she hid him for three months.' (Exodus 2 v 2)

Secret baby

24

For three long months, the Israelite mother kept her baby boy a secret.

But as he grew bigger, it was harder to hide him.

One day she sighed, 'I'll have to keep you somewhere else.'

She found a good, strong basket. To make sure it was waterproof, she painted it with tar. Then she wrapped up her baby, kissed him and put him inside.

'I hope no one sees!' she whispered to herself as she crept down to the river. And she hid the baby in the basket carefully among the tall reeds along the edge of the water.

God was watching over this special baby boy.

Have you ever played hide and seek? Where are some good places to hide in your house?

Pens Prayer

Dear Lord, You watch over me always, just as You watched over the baby in the basket. Thank You. Amen.

A Place to be Safe
The baby in the basket

Day 12

'The king's daughter came down to the river to bathe …' (Exodus 2 v 5)

The princess by the river

The secret baby boy had a sister. She stood a little way away from the river, and kept her eyes fixed on the basket.

'Whatever will happen?' she wondered.

Before long, she saw someone walking down to the water to bathe.

'It can't be!' gasped the baby's sister.

But it was! The king's daughter!

It was only a moment before the princess saw the basket in the reeds.

'What's that doing there?' she asked, and she told one of her servants to go and fetch it.

The princess spotted the basket, but God had His eyes on the baby, too.

Has anyone ever taken you paddling in a river or a stream?

Pens Prayer

Lord God, I praise You that You have promised You'll never leave me. Amen.

A Place to be Safe
The baby in the basket

Day 13

'The princess … saw a baby boy. He was crying, and she felt sorry for him.' (Exodus 2 v 6)

A royal surprise

The baby boy's sister gasped again.

'Oh, no!' she whispered to herself. 'If only the princess hadn't found my little brother. She'll take him to the king and he won't be safe any more!'

The princess peeped inside the basket.

The princess's eyes opened wide in surprise.

The princess smiled and cried, 'What a beautiful baby! A little Israelite boy! I shall make sure nothing happens to him. Don't worry, little man,' she added gently. 'I'll keep you safe.'

God sometimes sends other people to help His friends.

How would you feel if you ever met a princess?

Pens Prayer

Loving Lord, whenever someone needs help, I want to be ready to show them I care. Amen.

A Place to be Safe
The baby in the basket

Day 14

'Take this baby and nurse him for me, and I will pay you.' (Exodus 2 v 9)

Together again

'My baby brother's safe!' murmured the little boy's sister. She couldn't stop smiling!

Then she had an idea.

'Excuse me,' she said to the princess, timidly. 'I know someone who'd be very good at helping you take care of this little boy.'

'Then run and bring her to me straight away,' the princess replied.

And where did the baby boy's sister run? To her very own home to fetch her and her little brother's **VERY OWN MOTHER!**

'Look after this baby for me, please,' the princess said, and the baby's mother could hardly believe her ears.

God brought the baby and his mother together again.

If you were helping to look after a little baby, what sort of things would you need to do?

Pens Prayer

Father God, thank You for the people who look after me. Amen.

A Place to be Safe
The baby in the basket

Day 15

'… the king's daughter … adopted him as her own son.' (Exodus 2 v 10)

God's perfect plan

32

The baby in the basket was safe.

The baby in the basket was back in his mother's arms.

The baby in the basket didn't have to be hidden any longer.

When he was old enough, the princess adopted the little boy.

'I'll make sure you always have everything you need,' she said. 'And I'll call you, "Moses".'

The baby's mother and the baby's sister smiled to themselves.

God was happy, too. He'd never left Moses. Not for one second.

When the boy grew up, God would make him His special helper. Moses would rescue God's friends from Egypt.

 God always had a plan for the baby in the basket.

What name would you choose for a baby? Think of one for a boy and one for a girl.

Pens Prayer

Dear Lord, Your plans are always the very best. I know I am safe with You. Amen.

Day 16

GOD'S AMAZING GIFT

'… you will receive God's gift, the Holy Spirit.' (Acts 2 v 38)

'Humph,' Sharpy sighed, turning over in his basket.

'Foof,' he grunted, rolling back the other way.

His new friend, Stubbs, had gone home. Sharpy's basket wasn't the same without him.

'How can we help Sharpy feel better?' wondered Max.

'I know!' chirped Charlotte. 'Stubbs gave us all a special present – a bright, white stone. Why don't we let Sharpy keep it in his basket? It'll remind him how much Stubbs loves us.'

'Brilliant idea!' cried Max.

Sharpy thought it was brilliant, too. Having Stubbs' gift with him in his basket helped him feel close to his friend again.

God gives us the Holy Spirit to live inside us and help us stay close to Him.

Can you think of some of the presents you've been given for birthdays or Christmas?

Pens Prayer

Dear Father, thank You so much that You've given us Your Holy Spirit. What an amazing present! Amen.

God's Amazing Gift

'... the Father ... will give you another Helper [the Holy Spirit], who will stay with you for ever.' (John 14 v 16)

The feel-better letter

The sky was gloomy.
The weather was gloomy.
Pens were gloomy, too.
Except Philippa.

We've had a letter from Gordon and Stubbs!

"'Dear Friends,'" she read. "'We miss you, so we decided to send you a letter. We think Pens' town is lovely. Perhaps one day we'll be able to live there, too. Then we can see you every day. Lots of love from Gordon and Stubbs.'"

As Pens listened to the letter, huge smiles spread across their faces. The kind words made them all feel so much better – and the gloom slipped away.

God's Holy Spirit is like kind and loving words. He comforts and helps us.

Have you ever sent a letter or a card to someone?

From: Gordon and

Pens Prayer

Lord God, if I ever feel sad or lonely, help me remember that Your Holy Spirit is always with me to comfort me. Amen.

God's Amazing Gift

'The Helper, the Holy Spirit ... will teach you everything ...'
(John 14 v 26)

Finding the Way

Pens were at the fairground when they saw a maze made of paths and hedges.

'Let's go in,' cried Marco, 'and see how long it takes to find our way out!'

They took one path, then another and another – until at last –

'We're out!' cheered Marco.

'Where's Gloria?' asked Charlotte.

'I'm lost inside,' shrieked Gloria. 'I don't know how to get out!'

'Don't worry!' called Marco. 'I'll keep talking to you. Follow my voice and it'll lead you the right way.'

So Gloria listened and followed, and Marco's voice guided her safely out of the maze.

 When we ask Him to, the Holy Spirit will lead us through each day. He will help us understand how to live the way God wants us to.

Did you know that you can talk to the Holy Spirit in the same way as you talk to God?

Pens Prayer

Lord, please teach me to follow Your Holy Spirit day after day. Amen.

Day 19   God's Amazing Gift

'He is the Spirit who reveals the truth about God.'
(John 14 v 17)

The best teacher

'Where's Miss Fountain Pen?' wondered Squiggle and Splodge.

They sat in the school classroom, waiting.

But another teacher arrived instead because Miss Fountain Pen wasn't well.

'I hope she's better soon,' sighed Splodge. 'School's not the same without her.'

'Not the same at all,' agreed Squiggle. 'Miss Fountain Pen teaches us how to read and write, paint and sing, plant seeds, make puppets, and SO MUCH MORE! She's always smiling and always helpful.'

'Let's make her a get well soon card,' suggested Splodge. 'We can write "thank you" in it as well, for being such an amazing teacher.'

The Holy Spirit is our Teacher. He helps us learn about God and understand the stories in the Bible.

What have you learnt about at your school or pre-school this week?

Pens Prayer

Thank You, Father God, for giving me Your Holy Spirit, who helps me get to know You better. Amen.

God's Amazing Gift

'… let the Spirit direct your lives …' (Galatians 5 v 16)

Denzil's bike race

Denzil was entering a bike race.

I'm sure I can win, unless Max and Marco enter. I won't win then because they're faster than I am.

So Denzil didn't tell Max and Marco about the race.

'Hey, Denzil!' grinned Marco. 'We're going swimming. Want to come?'

'Yo, Denzil!' called Max. 'Afterwards we're going skateboarding. Come along!'

Max and Marco were always inviting Denzil to join in. Suddenly he realised it was unkind not tell them about the bike race.

'Let's go!' Denzil smiled. 'And there's a bike race soon. We should all do it together.'

 God's Holy Spirit inside us helps us do the right thing instead of the wrong thing.

Cycling is one way to race. What other sorts of races can you think of?

Pens Prayer

Dear Lord, I want to do good and kind things, not bad and selfish things. Help me to listen to Your Holy Spirit inside me. Amen.

God's Amazing Gift

'The Spirit ... must also control our lives.'
(Galatians 5 v 25)

A grumpy headache

One morning, Charlotte had a headache. It wasn't a bad headache, but just enough to make her feel grumpy.

Put a cold flannel on your forehead. I find that helps when *I've* got a headache.

Flann

Day 22

God's Amazing Gift

'... if I have no love, I am nothing.' (1 Corinthians 13 v 2)

Time to be kind

Something had arrived at Squiggle and Splodge's house in a cardboard box. A red, shiny swing with a sky-blue seat!

It's here!

THIS WAY UP

46

'I can't wait to put it together,' giggled Splodge.

But the putting it together was the problem.

'We need help,' sighed Squiggle.

Gloria hurried past.

'Could you help us, please?' Squiggle asked.

'No time!' bustled Gloria.

Squiggle and Splodge's faces fell.

'All right,' Gloria smiled. She didn't like to see them looking disappointed. 'Let's see what I can do. If I can make hats, I'm sure I can help you make a swing.'

The Holy Spirit inside us helps us show love to each other and to God.

Do you like making things? What have you made?

Pens Prayer

Dear God, I pray Your Holy Spirit will teach me to be loving and patient – just like You. Amen.

Day 23 God's Amazing Gift

'… the Spirit produces love, joy, peace, patience, kindness, goodness, faithfulness, humility, and self-control.' (Galatians 5 v 22–23)

As good as they look

Philippa's tree was covered in round, rosy apples. They were beautiful and shiny and they looked delicious.

Marco lay on his back on the grass trying to count them.

'Philippa,' said Marco, 'your tree has more apples than I've ever seen!'

'That's because I try to look after it and give it exactly what it needs,' Philippa replied. 'Then it can grow lots of lovely fruit. Pick one, if you like.'

Marco picked an apple and took a big bite. It was crisp and juicy.

'Yum!' he munched. 'These apples really are as good as they look!'

 We need the Holy Spirit to help us grow into the kind of people God wants us to be.

What other fruits grow on trees? Can you think of any that grow on smaller plants and bushes?

Day 24 — God's Amazing Gift

'... you cannot bear fruit unless you remain in me.'
(John 15 v 4)

Denzil was singing.

'Don't usually hear *you* singing,' Max remarked.

Denzil replied, 'Must be because I spend lots of time with Charlotte.'

Squiggle was playing with a ball.

'Don't usually see *you* playing ball,' commented Marco.

Squiggle said, 'Must be because I spend lots of time throwing balls for Sharpy.'

Philippa was wearing a hat.

'Don't usually see *you* wearing a hat,' smiled Splodge.

Philippa answered, 'Must be because I spend lots of time with Gloria. Being with someone a lot means the things *they* do and say can make a difference to the things *you* do and say.'

 The more time we spend with God and His Son, Jesus, the more the Holy Spirit can help us to be like Them.

Do you have friends you spend lots of time with? What do you like to do together?

Pens Prayer

Father God, I want to spend time with You every day, so that Your Holy Spirit can help me grow more like You every day. Amen.

THE PLANTING PARABLE
Growing for God

Day 25

'The crowd that gathered round [Jesus] was so large that he got into a boat …' (Mark 4 v 1)

Jesus on the lake

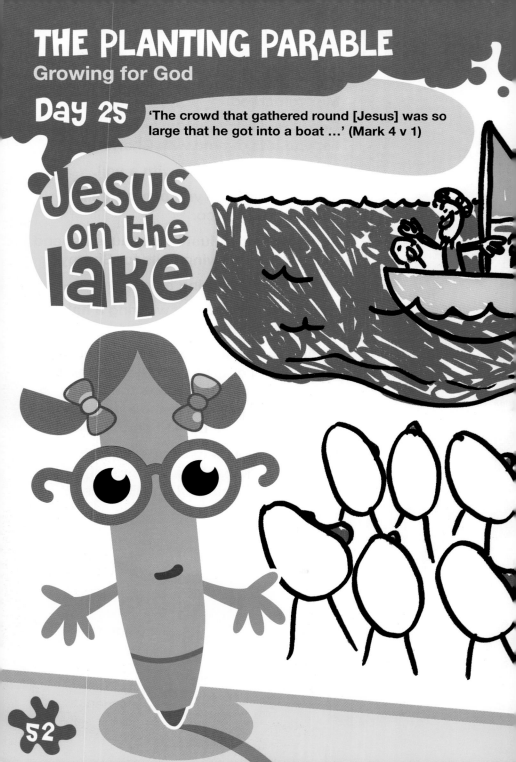

Jesus was teaching beside Lake Galilee. When people heard He was there, the crowd of listeners grew bigger and bigger.

So many wanted to hear what He had to say.

So many wanted to listen to the stories He would tell.

So many wanted to learn about God.

There was a boat on the lake behind Jesus. It bobbed gently up and down. Jesus knew He needed to be somewhere where more of the crowd could see Him. He jumped into the boat, pushed out across the water and taught the people from Lake Galilee.

Jesus wanted to teach as many people as possible about God.

How many different types of boat can you think of?

Pens Prayer

Thank You so much, Lord God, for sending Jesus to teach us all about You. Amen.

Day 26

'Once there was a man who went out to sow corn.' (Mark 4 v 3)

Roots and shoots

'Let me tell you a story about a farmer,' Jesus began. 'As he planted his corn seeds, some of them fell on the path round his field.

'"No good there," said the farmer. "The birds will eat them up."

'The farmer was right. The birds did.

'Some more of the seeds dropped among stones where there wasn't much earth. Soon, little green shoots began to spring up.

'"No good there," said the farmer. "There's not enough soil for proper roots."

'The farmer was right. When the hot sun began to shine, the tiny new plants quickly dried up.'

Seeds need to be planted in good, deep earth if they're going to be able to grow.

Lots of plants grow from seeds. Do you know what else they grow from?

Pens Prayer

Dear God, thank You for seeds that give us beautiful flowers and food to eat. Amen.

The Planting Parable
Growing for God

Day 27

'But some seeds fell in good soil, and the plants sprouted, grew, and produced corn ...' (Mark 4 v 8)

Just the right place

Jesus carried on telling His planting story.

'The farmer scattered more seeds,' He said, 'but some of them landed among weeds. When the seeds' tiny green shoots appeared, they only just managed to grow up between them.

'"No good there," said the farmer. "They haven't enough space and light and water."

'The farmer was right. The plants were too weak to grow corn.

'But some seeds,' Jesus continued, 'fell in just the right place.

'"Perfect," smiled the farmer. "The soil there is good and deep. Those seeds will give lots of golden corn."

'The farmer was right. They did.'

When seeds have what they need to grow, they can produce their wonderful flowers and fruit.

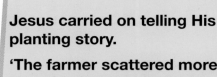

What's your favourite fruit and favourite vegetable?

Pens Prayer

Thank You God, for good earth where our plants and trees can grow. Amen.

The Planting Parable
Growing for God

Day 28

'The sower sows God's message.' (Mark 4 v 14)

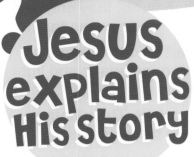

Some of the people who had heard Jesus' story about the farmer went to speak to Him.

'We don't understand, Jesus,' they said. 'What does Your story mean?'

Jesus smiled. 'The seeds the farmer is planting in My story stand for God's message,' He answered. 'That message is everything I teach you about God, and everything you read about Him.

'As the farmer plants the seeds, they land in different places on the ground. In the same way, different kinds of people hear about God. Some want to be His friends but, sadly, others don't care about Him.'

Jesus' stories helped people understand God's message.

Do you know a story really well? Why not see if you can tell it to someone?

Pens Prayer

Lord, help me to understand the stories You told in the Bible. Amen.

The Planting Parable
Growing for God

Day 29

'Other people are like the seeds that fall on rocky ground ... they hear the message ... But it does not sink deep into them ...' (Mark 4 v 16–17)

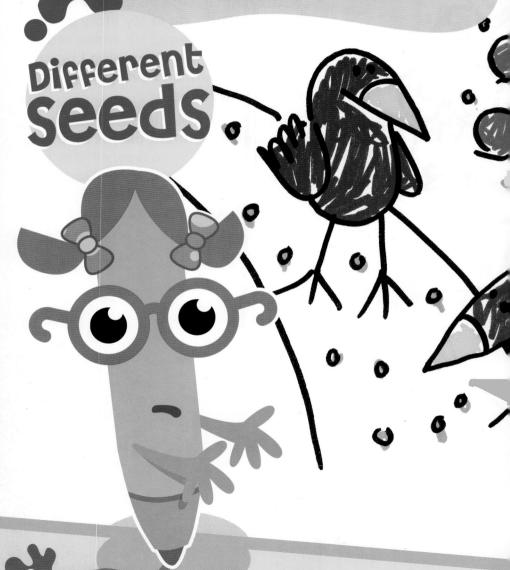

Different seeds

'When some people hear about God,' Jesus said, 'they are like the farmer's seeds that fell onto the path and were eaten by birds.

'They don't want to hear God's message.

'They take no notice, and they won't make friends with Him.

'Other people who hear about God are like the seeds dropped among stones. They start to grow, but then dry up very quickly. God's message makes them happy at first, but they don't stay close to Him.

'They don't keep praying.

'When they have bad days and sad days, they forget about God.'

Jesus wanted people to know how important it is to stay close to God.

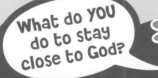

What do YOU do to stay close to God?

Pens Prayer

Dear Lord, I want to be Your friend every day, just as You want to be my Friend every day. Amen.

The Planting Parable
Growing for God

Day 30

'But other people are like the seeds sown in good soil. They hear the message, accept it, and bear fruit ...' (Mark 4 v 20)

Seeds of a smile

'Remember the seeds that landed in weeds?' Jesus asked. 'They grew, but they didn't produce corn. The weeds were too big and strong. Those seeds are like people who hear about God, but don't learn to trust Him.

'They worry. They don't make time for Him.'

Then Jesus smiled. 'But some people listen to God and ask Him to be their Friend. They tell others about His love and they know they'll be with Him forever.

'They are like the seeds that fell in good earth and grew golden corn.

'They are the seeds that make God smile.'

God wants us to trust Him. He will never leave us.

What makes you smile?

Pens Prayer

Please help me, Father, to grow up close to You. I want to make You smile. Amen.

Pens titles

More *Pens* for you to enjoy

- ★ Friends
- ★ Father God
- ★ Following Jesus
- ★ Really Special
- ★ Trusting God
- ★ Helping and Serving

- ★ Big and Small
- ★ God's Book
- ★ God's Love
- ★ God Cares
- ★ God's Heroes
- ★ Thank You God

Pens Special!
Christmas

The *Pens* characters tell the Christmas story to make Jesus' birth real and memorable for young children. Also with five days of Bible-reading notes.

Pens Special!
Starting School

Help children start school confidently, knowing that God goes there with them. A short story followed by five days of Bible notes.

For current prices visit
www.cwr.org.uk/store

Available online, or from your local Christian bookshop.

Coming January 2012:
Pens Special! Easter